Comedy S...

Morecambe ~~and Wise~~

Eddie Braben
adapted by Bill Ridgway

M
Macmillan Education

First published 1986

Published by
MACMILLAN EDUCATION LTD
Houndmills, Basingstoke, Hampshire RG21 2XS
and London
Companies and representatives
throughout the world

Designed by Milford Hurley

Typeset by Vine & Gorfin Ltd, Exmouth, Devon
Printed in Hong Kong

British Library Cataloguing in Publication Data
Braben, Eddie (Barker, Ronnie)
Morecambe and Wise.—(Comedy scripts)
1. Readers—1950–
I. Title   II. Ridgway, Bill   III. Series
428.6'2   PE1126.D4
ISBN 0-333-40922-1

Acknowledgement
The author and publishers wish to thank the BBC
for giving permission to use the photographs
included in this book.

Contents

The Nose Job

(*Eric is sitting up in a hospital bed. He has a dressing over his nose. A nurse enters through swing doors.*)

Nurse: Are you feeling better?

Eric: (*Touches nose*) Still a bit sore, but there's one thing that's worrying me.

Nurse: What's that?

Eric: Well, when a man has his nose changed, do you think he's being a bit . . . well . . .

Nurse: Stuck-up?

Eric: Yes.

Nurse: Certainly not, Mr Morecambe.

Eric: Good.

Nurse: I'll show Mr Wise in. (*Moves to doors*) I'll be back soon to take the dressing off. (*She goes out.*)

Eric: He'll have a good laugh at me, now. And I'm sitting here just asking for it.

(*Ernie enters. He is trying not to laugh.*)

Ernie: How's the nose, then? When's the dressing coming off?

Eric: Stop grinning.

Ernie: I'm not grinning. It's not very funny when a man gets a new conk.

Eric: It's not a conk.

Ernie: How do you feel?

Eric: Not too bad.

Ernie: How about your snitch?

Eric: It isn't a snitch. Why don't you come in here and have your legs stretched on the National Health?

Ernie: I thought they only did hooters. Hooters, snitches and conks.

Eric: It isn't a hooter. Watch it, because I'm coming out today.

Ernie: That's the thanks I get for coming in to cheer you up. I've brought you a present.

(*Gives him present.*)

Eric: Very kind. What is it?

Ernie: Snuff! (*Laughs*) Big job, was it?

Eric: A three-hour operation.

Ernie: It was a big snitch.

Eric: You think you're funny, don't you? Just wait till I get out of here.

Ernie: It's been puzzling me for days now.

Eric: What has?

Ernie: What did they do with the old one?

Eric: What old one?

Ernie: I'd like your old nose. I could use it as a paperweight.

Eric: I'm warning you.

(*Ernie stops at the bedside table and picks up a beaker. He puts it on his nose.*)

Eric: I won't tell you again. It's time you were leaving.

Ernie: No, I'm staying to see what the new one looks like.

Eric: Then shut up and stop having a go at me.

Ernie: I won't say a word.

(*Ernie crosses to the window and looks out.*)

That factory across the road.

Eric: What about it?

Ernie: The hooter's gone.

Eric: Just lay off – that's all.

Ernie: I won't say a word. (*Begins singing.*) 'Nobody *knows* the trouble I've seen,.........'

Eric: Shut up.

Ernie: All right to smoke in here?

Eric: It's not allowed.

Ernie: Pity. I could just do with a *snout*.

Eric: (*Shouts*) Get out!

(*Nurse enters.*)

Nurse: You two are making a lot of noise.

Eric: Just get him out of here.

Nurse: Mr Wise, have you been upsetting Mr Morecambe?

Ernie: Me, nurse?

(*Ernie looks innocent.*)

Nurse: (*Looks at Ern.*) No, I don't suppose it's you. This is the moment we've all been waiting for.

(*She starts to undo Eric's dressing.*)

Eric: Not before time.

Ernie: I'll bet they felt like this the first time they brought Concorde out of the hangar.

Eric: What's it like? How do I look now? Does it make a difference? Be honest, now.

Ernie: I like it.

Eric: Good. Is it like 007's?

Nurse: Have a look in the hand mirror. (*Gives mirror to Eric.*)

4

Eric: (*Looks at himself in mirror: throws it away.*) What's he done? This is not what I wanted.

Ernie: It's going to get a lot of laughs.

Eric: Get him out.

Nurse: Mr Wise, I must ask you to leave.

Ernie: Sorry. (*Ernie goes out, laughing.*)

Eric: (*Getting out of bed, and walking to the doors*) By the way . . . .

(*As Ernie comes in again Eric pushes the swing door and hits Ernie in the face. Ernie enters holding his nose.*)

Ernie: My nose! You've broken it!

Eric: In here, Big Mouth.

(*Eric pushes Ernie into the bed and throws the blankets over him.*)

Package Holiday

(*Scene: Lounge in the flat. Eric and Ernie sitting on the settee, with a pile of magazines.*)

Eric: What are those?

Ernie: Travel mags. (*Takes them from bag.*)

Eric: You don't have to emigrate. Take no notice of what they say about you.

Ernie: I need a good holiday. Plenty of rest and lots and lots of sunshine.

Eric: What about Blackpool?

Ernie: Blackpool! I'm not going to Blackpool. I want something more exciting than Blackpool.

Eric: I like Blackpool.

Ernie: That's you all over. Afraid to try anything different. Do you fancy horse riding?

Eric: No! I'd hurt your back.

Ernie: You've never been abroad, have you?

Eric: Yes.

Ernie: The Isle of Man doesn't count.

Eric: No, I haven't.

Ernie: It sounds good in Spain. (*Reading*) 'Wake up in your hotel and listen to the sound of the sea.......'

Eric: '... as it laps against your bed.' I've heard about those Spanish hotels.

Ernie: Well, I fancy Spain.

Eric: Will you visit the Pyramids?

Ernie: I'm going to Spain – not America.

Eric: Can you speak Spanish?

Ernie: Sí.

Eric: We'll get a long way on that. What do you want to go abroad for?

Ernie: I need a holiday abroad. I want to feel the sun on my back.

Eric: Too much sun's not good for you.

Ernie: Look, what's *your* idea? What would *you* say was the best holiday?

Eric: I'll tell you what. A pair of boots and a back-pack, and over the hills for a month.

Ernie: You wouldn't last five minutes.

Eric: Not me, *you*. I'd go to Blackpool.

Ernie: Oh Spain! Just think of those sandy beaches and the warm sea.

Eric: I don't care about sandy beaches and the warm sea.

Ernie: The young, brown-eyed, Spanish girls.

Eric: How long does it take to get there?

Ernie: I've just thought. It's just come to me why you don't care about the sandy beaches and the warm sea.

Eric: That's got nothing to do with it.

Ernie: (*Smiling*) Who can't swim, then?

Eric: I *can* swim.

Ernie: You can't swim and you're scared stiff of water.

Eric: Shut up, you.

Ernie: I can still remember when we went to the baths with the school.

(*Laughing*)

Eric: You're asking for one, you are.

Ernie: You went in the water and they shouted 'who threw those bones in?' (*Laughing*) And those skinny legs – like two cigarettes.

Eric: You can talk, Dumpy.

Ernie: I'm not Dumpy.

Eric: Dumpy Wise!

Ernie: I've got a beautiful body, I have.

Eric: If you go in the water, don't swim on your back or they'll build an oil rig on you.

Ernie: What about this holiday? You tell me where you'd like to go.

Eric: I'm in no hurry to go anywhere.

Ernie: Well, you can please yourself – I'm going to Spain. (*Opening bag.*)

Eric: What's in there?

Ernie: Holiday gear.

(*Holds up a tiny pair of swimming shorts.*)

Look at those.

Eric: What are they?

Ernie: Swimming shorts. It should be clear to anyone.

Eric: Put them on and it will be. You're not going to wear those on the beach, are you?

Ernie: Yes, I'm going to wear those on the beach in Spain.

Eric: I hope for your sake you know the Spanish for 'How dare you , sir'.

Ernie: I got them from that new shop. It's called The In Place.

Eric: 'The In Place'? They'll *put* you in if you wear those. There was nothing wrong with your old suit. It only needed the elbow mending.

Ernie: Well, I'm looking forward to the food.

Eric: That Spanish rubbish.

Ernie: I like Spanish food.

Eric: Have you decided on a hotel yet, Ern?

Ernie: This one. (*Points to a picture.*) Each room overlooks a swimming pool ringed with palm trees.

Eric: (*Looks at magazine.*) Have you seen what it says underneath? It's not been put up yet.

Ernie: It will be by the time I get there.

Eric: So long as you don't mind sleeping in a builder's shed.

Ernie: (*Smiling*) I won't be doing much sleeping, will I?

Eric: How do you mean?

Ernie: The night spots.

Eric: You'll be covered in them.

Ernie: Night clubs, watching those Spanish dancers.

(*Ernie does a Spanish dance.*)

It really hurts the back of your legs.

Eric: Spanish dancing! What a load of rubbish.

Ernie: You won't put me off. Lying on top of the bed at night. A warm breeze blowing in from the sea . . . looking up at the stars . . . .

Eric: Through the hole in the roof.

Ernie: My mind's made up. There are lots of new places to see. I might go to Granada.

Eric: The BBC won't like that. You'd better take these. (*Gives him the bathing trunks.*) You can fill them with peanuts and hang them out for the blue-tits.

Ernie: You know the best thing about this holiday? It's cheap.

Eric: How cheap?

Ernie: £60 all in.

Eric: All in one bed. (*Looks through the magazine, then stops at one page.*) Did you say £60?

Ernie: That's right.

Eric: Have you read the rest – on page 74?

Ernie: I couldn't care less.

Eric: It says: (*Reading*) 'Since this list came out, fuel and airport charges have gone up. This means that an extra £40 must be added.'

Ernie: £40 and £60? That's £100.

Eric: That's close.

Ernie: I have made up my mind. Away at 10.30 in the morning.

Eric: Plane?

Ernie: Train.

Eric: Spain?

Ernie: Blackpool.

Eric: I'll come with you.

Haunted House

(Cottage room with a staircase. Sound of a car coming to a halt, car doors slamming. Door opens: Eric and Ernie enter and look around.)

Ernie: This is it, Eric. It's supposed to be over 500 years old. Where's that taxi driver?

Eric: He's coming with the luggage.

(Taxi driver enters with the cases.)

Driver: The luggage, gentlemen. £1 please.

Eric: A good price. You can have it.

Ernie: If you'll just take them up to the bedroom, please.

(The driver is so shocked he drops the cases.)

Driver: No! Not up those stairs, sir. Not after what happened in this house. No! I can't stop here. I'm off . . .

(Pulls himself together and tries to hide his fear.)

    . . . what I mean is, I have to pick up my wife.

Eric: Why – does she keep falling down?

Driver: No, I've got to mend the car . . . meet my mates . . . I'm not staying in this house any longer. Pay me the money.

Ernie: We'll pay you as soon as you've told us what it is about this cottage that scares you.

Driver: Well, if you're staying here you have a right to know. Sit down, gentlemen.

(They sit at the table.)

12

It was 6 July 1874. Two brothers lived in this cottage then. One was a little dumpy lad who was always writing. The other was a tall lad with specs. Going a bit thin on top. He was always ready with a joke and he had a head full of cobwebs. You know the kind.

Eric: No.

Ernie: Yes . . . What happened? We might as well hear the rest of this rubbish.

Driver: It was on a night like this that the two lads went up to bed. The church clock struck midnight and then there were screams as if the devil himself had come. A passing woodcutter heard the screams and rushed up those stairs. The sight that met his eyes was too awful for words. It turned him into a fool for the rest of his days.

Eric: (*Scared*) How do you mean?

Driver: The two lads lay dead across the bed. They were all twisted up, like. And there was something that was never explained.

Eric: (*Swallows hard*) Oh?

Driver: Scratch marks.

Eric: Scratch marks?

Driver: Torn across the flesh of their bodies. Scratch marks on the wall, around the window. They had been 'visited' that night. It was their eyes – popping out of their heads . . . .
My money, please – £1. I want to get off home.

Ernie: Here you are. £1.02. And keep the change.

(*Ernie gives the driver the money. The driver crosses to the door and turns.*)

Driver: That is why folks round here call this place Death Cottage.

(*The driver goes out. A long pause: Eric and Ernie look at each other. Eric gets up and quickly goes to the door.*)

Ernie: Where are you going?

Eric: Scotland.

Ernie: Pull yourself together and make a cup of tea.

(*Eric goes to the sink and works the pump: very brown water comes out.*)

Eric: I hope you like your tea strong.

Ernie: I'm not drinking that. Pour me a drink.

(*Eric crosses to the table and tries to pour a drink: his hands shake.*)

Ernie: You're shaking.

Eric: No, I'm not. I've got loose bones.

Ernie: You believed everything that taxi driver told you, and you're scared.

Eric: I'm not scared. I've got you to look after me. Kung Fu.

Ernie: Get the cases and take them upstairs to the bedroom.

(Eric gets the cases.)

Eric: *(Scared)* Is it the same bedroom?

Ernie: Yes, where those two men were murdered.

(Eric moves to the stairs, then comes back.)

Eric: Can I leave them outside the bedroom door?

Ernie: No, take them inside, but mind the two dead bodies in the bed.

(Eric goes upstairs. Ernie stays at the table, then gets up and goes to the bottom of the stairs.)

(Quietly) Eric . . . . Eric.

(Pause)

(Knock on the door. Ernie goes to the door and opens it.)

Good Lord. What are you doing here?

(We see Eric standing at the door.)

Eric: I fell out of the bedroom window.

(Ernie grabs Eric and pushes him upstairs.)

The Sick-bed

(Medicine bottles are on the table. Ernie, wearing a dressing gown, on the settee looking ill. Eric enters from the kitchen.)

Eric: How are you feeling?

Ernie: Terrible.

Eric: The doctor will be here soon. I rang him this morning. He said it sounds as if you've got the 'flu, but you know him. He'll say anything for a laugh. I went to see him last week. He said, 'I haven't seen you in years.' I said, 'I know, I've been ill.' *(Laughs to himself.)*

(Ernie sneezes.)

That's amazing that is.

Ernie: It was only a sneeze.

Eric: I know, but every time you sneeze it lifts your wig off your head. You can see daylight.

Ernie: I thought I'd get a few kind words. I should have known better.

Eric: Cheer up, Ern. I've got a nice bowl of chicken soup here.

Ernie: *(Sitting up)* Oh, good.

Eric: *(Starting to drink the soup)* I've got to keep my strength up. There's a lot of 'flu about. It's a nasty thing, 'flu.

Ernie: You don't have to tell me.

Eric: You can die from 'flu.

Ernie: Thanks very much.

Eric: I've got nothing to worry about. I had a 'flu jab in my arm last week.

Ernie: You'll still get it.

Eric: But my arm won't (*Eric carries on eating soup*) You need food, and plenty of it. Why don't you warm up some soup for yourself?

Ernie: I'm too weak to walk to the kitchen.

Eric: You can crawl can't you? Crawl on your belly. It won't take you long. It's lovely soup, Ern.

Ernie: (*Watching Eric.*) I wouldn't mind a bit of your bread dipped in that soup.

Eric: (*Picking up bread.*) A bit of bread dipped in this soup?

Ernie: Yes, please.

(*Eric dips bread in soup and eats it.*)

Eric: No, you wouldn't like it.

(*He finishes and takes the tray to the hatch.*)

You must be ill. You haven't written a play for half-an-hour.

Ernie: You seem to forget that even someone as clever as I am can catch 'flu. I'll write six plays tomorrow.

Eric: Only six?

Ernie: I might be going out in the afternoon.

Eric: I keep forgetting that. But you've got to take care. You can die of 'flu. I think you'd better have another powder.

Ernie: Must I?

Eric: If you want to get well again. (*Through the hatch*) Is the powder ready for Mr Wise, please?

Ernie: If you're going to give me a powder, just give it to me and stop messing about.

(Eric comes back to Ernie.)

Eric: Open up. I've got your sweet ready.

(Ernie opens his mouth and Eric blows powder into it.)

Ernie: Horrible! A sweet! Quick, a sweet!

Eric: What?

Ernie: A sweet, quick.

Eric: Good Lord, I've dropped it.

(Picks up the sweet and gives it to Ernie.)

Ernie: Oh, I hate those powders. Where did you get them?

Eric: The new chemist.

Ernie: The new chemist?

Eric: Yes, it's got his name on the packet.

Ernie: *(Reading)* Bob Martin?

Eric: Yes.

Ernie: *(Louder)* Bob Martin!

Eric: Do you know him?

Ernie: *(Very loud)* Bob Martin!!

Eric: Do you know him that well?

Ernie: You've been giving me dog powders.

Eric: I haven't. Sit! Sit! I wasn't sure whether you had the 'flu or dog fleas.

Ernie: Oh, I feel weak. Could I have another pillow, please?

Eric: You haven't finished that one yet.

Ernie: Go and see if the doctor's coming.

Eric: Right. *(Crosses to the window and looks out.)* Not yet

(Ernie moans.)

Eric: (*Crossing back to Ernie.*) You feel ill, do you?

Ernie: Really ill.

Eric: Really ill?

Ernie: Yes.

Eric: I thought so. That's why I knew you wouldn't mind.

Ernie: Wouldn't mind what?

(*Eric sits down on Ernie's legs.*)

Ernie: Get off my legs!

Eric: (*Sitting down again.*) Now's as good a time as any to ask you. Have you made a Will yet, Ern?

Ernie: What?

Eric: A Will, leaving everything to me because I've been so kind to you over the years.

Ernie: *You've* been so kind to me over the years?

Eric: I'm glad you agree. Just put that in writing here. (*Puts the Will on the table.*)

Ernie: What's that thing?

Eric: A Will.

Ernie: A Will?

Eric: Yes. I got it from Woolworths. It was between the Easter eggs and the Christmas cards.

Ernie: I never heard of anything so horrible in my life.

Eric: Goodness, Ern, what do you mean?

Ernie: You poison me with dog powders and now you want me to make my Will out to you. Get lost! I'm not ready to die yet.

(*Coughs*)

Eric: I know that, Ern. You could last for two more days yet. Just write at the top, 'I, Ernie Wise . . . .'

Ernie: No!

Eric: You've got to put that down or I won't get all your money.

Ernie: (*Staggering to his feet.*) All my money to you! Give me that thing.

(*Staggers towards Eric who is holding the Will.*)

Eric: You fool! You'll make yourself worse. Come on, try to get it.

Ernie: (*Hand to head.*) The room's spinning and my legs are going.

(*Falls on to the settee.*)

Eric: Make it out now. Come on, don't be so selfish! Make your Will out to me.

Ernie: Get off my legs. You can't wait for me to go, can you? I thought you were my friend and all this time you've been waiting to get your grubby little hands on my money.

Eric: I'm broke! Why don't you die? You're too selfish, you are.

Ernie: To think that all this time you've been planning it.

Eric: I haven't.

(*Doorbell*)

Ernie: Thank goodness, the doctor at last.

Eric: I don't think it's the doctor. (*Crosses to door.*)

Ernie: What do you mean?

(*Eric opens the door and an undertaker comes into the flat.*)

Undertaker: I believe you have a . . . . . .

Eric: Not yet! Call back in half-an-hour! We're still polishing the wood.

(*Pushes him out and closes the door.*)

Ernie: I don't believe it! I saw it with my own eyes and I don't believe it!

Eric: I don't know what you're talking about.

Ernie: Who was that man?

Eric: What man?

Ernie: The man who just came to the door.

Eric: What door . . . ? Oh *that* man!

Ernie: Yes, *that* man.

Eric: He wasn't an undertaker!

Ernie: He was.

Eric: No! He just called to see if we had any empty boxes.

(*Eric walks round.*)

Ernie: Don't talk to me. I've had my fill of you, I have. You're not getting my money.

Eric: Think about it! If you don't leave it to me the Government will get it.

Ernie: I'd rather *they* got it than you!

Eric: Now what's the Government going to do with a teddy bear and a trunk full of wigs? You might as well leave it to me. You haven't got any family.

Ernie: I'm not leaving you a penny and that's the end of it.

Eric: I see. (*Gets up and walks behind the settee.*) Can I have a quick look at your papers?

Ernie: You'll never find where I've hidden them.

(*Eric takes the papers out of the hunting horn.*)

It doesn't matter, there's nothing for you.

Eric: You've been paying 5p a week on this one.

Ernie: Yes. I took it all out when I was 21.

Eric: It says here that if you die you get £7.50

Ernie: It'll come in handy, that will.

Eric: It'll pay for the ham tea, and that's about all.

Ernie: And I like a nice bit of ham.

Eric: It says that if you die you get £7.50 and £15 if you die twice. Now that's what I call good.

Ernie: It's an excellent firm.

Eric: It says here that if you get struck by lightning you get £25 000.

Ernie: That's right.

Eric: (*Looks through window.*) It looks a bit dull. How do you feel about standing on the roof for half-an-hour?

Ernie: How many times do you want telling? Now put those papers back.

Eric: I'm the best friend you've got.

Ernie: You can say that? After the tricks you've tried to pull?

Eric: I think a lot of you. You're like a brother to me.

Ernie: You've got a funny way of showing it.

Eric: I'll just say this once. I think a lot of you and I wouldn't do anything to upset you.

Ernie: I think you mean that.

Eric: Anything that I've done here today has been done to try and cheer you up because you've got the 'flu.

Ernie: And I really went for you, didn't I?

Eric: If it's made you feel any better, Ern, I don't mind what you say to me. You can even hit me if you like. Go on, hit me if it cheers you up.

(*Ernie hits Eric.*)

Ernie: Give me that Will. (*Eric quickly gives the Will to Ernie.*) You're right, you are the only friend I've got.

Eric: You don't *have* to leave anything to me, Ern. (*Clicks Ern's pen.*)

Ernie: But I'm going to, Eric. I know you're a fine friend. (*Is about to write when the doorbell rings.*) That'll be the doctor.

Eric: It might not be. Sign your name. (*Crosses to the door and a young lady comes in, carrying flowers.*)

Florist: Good morning. You ordered flowers . . . .

Eric: Call back in about half-an-hour. (*Pushes the girl out of the flat and closes the door.*)

Ernie: You evil, wicked man!

Eric: I thought it was Christmas. I was going to put them in a vase.

Ernie: You rotten . . . she was from the flower shop.

Eric: She wasn't.

Ernie: I saw her!

Eric: It was the coalman!

Ernie: The coalman dressed like that?

Eric: Yes, it's his day off!

Ernie: If only you knew how you look right now. It's really funny. (*Laughing*)

Eric: Stop laughing and be ill.

Ernie: It's cheered me up and I feel much better.

Eric: That's just you, that is! Self, self, self all the time. Don't just sit there – roll over and die!

Ernie: I feel great now! (*Laughing*) First the undertaker, then the girl from the flower shop. (*Laughing*) Do you know any more jokes like that? (*Laughing*)

Eric: Please, Ern, I don't feel too good. (*Hand to head*)

Ernie: You've got it – you've caught the 'flu!

Eric: My legs are all wobbly and the room's spinning.

(*Flops on to the settee.*)

Ernie: Great! Marvellous! Go on. Be really ill, don't be selfish! (*Doorbell rings*) That'll be the doctor, I'll let him in.

(*Opens the door and the doctor enters.*)

Doctor: Are you the patient?

Ernie: Not now, doctor. (*Both cross to a sad-looking Eric.*)

Doctor: Hello, Mr Morecambe. I haven't seen you for a long time.

Ernie: No, he's been ill.

Doctor: Let's have a look at you.

Ernie: Before you examine him doctor, (*Picks up the Will and pen and gives them to Eric*) Just write down – I, Eric Morecambe . . . .

Growing Old

(Eric is lying on top of the bed. He has dressing gown on over his pyjamas. He is reading a book and eating wine gums from a paper bag. He looks up as Ernie enters and is drying his face with a towel. Ernie has dressing gown on.)

Eric: Had a bath then?

Ernie: Yes.

Eric: It's not September, is it? By golly, how time flies.

Ernie: No jokes at this time of the night, please.

Eric: It's funny you should mention jokes.

Ernie: You've just thought of one.

Eric: A belter. Fancy a wine gum before I tell it?

Ernie: I don't like wine gums. What's this joke you've thought of?

Eric: There's this man, he goes on his holidays and when he arrives at the digs the ladlady says to him, 'Do you like lamb?' When he goes upstairs . . . .

Ernie: He finds four sheep in his bedroom.

Eric: *(Annoyed)* Do you want a fight?

Ernie: You're not the only one who reads the *Beano*. Just for once let's have no more jokes tonight, I'm worn out.

(Ernie removes his dressing gown. He is wearing underneath a long-sleeved vest with buttons up to the neck and a very baggy pair of long johns.)

Eric: *(Laughing)* How long have you been wearing them, Grandad?

Ernie: Don't make fun.

Eric: It's a joke! You're trying a joke out on me for the next show.

Ernie: I'm not wearing them for a joke.

Eric: They make me laugh. Go and have a look in the mirror.

Ernie: I have to look after my health, I have a very delicate chest. I paid a lot of money for these, they're government rejects.

Eric: You could get the whole of the government in there, and there'd still be room at the back for a few more members.

Ernie: These are all-wool ex-naval officer's underwear.

Eric: Ex-naval officers? Turn round . . . you're right, there's a porthole at the back.

Ernie: Let me get my pyjamas on.

(Ernie puts his pyjamas on over the underwear.)

Eric: You're not going to bed like that, are you? That's a proper old man's trick that is!

(Ernie climbs into bed.)

Ernie: Sticks and stones.

Eric: I know what's behind all this namby-pamby bit, looking after yourself. Do you know what your trouble is?

Ernie: You tell me.

Eric: Your trouble is you're afraid of growing old.

Ernie: *(Angry and sits up in bed.)* That's not true! I'm not afraid of growing old!

Eric: Ern, you can't fight nature, it's been proved by cleverer men than me.

Ernie: What has?

26

Eric: Exactly. And I'll tell you something else now that you've asked.

Ernie: What?

Eric: You're sitting on my wine gums.

Ernie: Goodnight!

Eric: Let's face it, you've got this fear about growing old. Did I ever tell you about my Uncle Barney?

Ernie: What has your Uncle Barney got to do with it?

Eric: His father, Jethroe Morecambe, discovered the secret of long life.

Ernie: Discovered the secret of long life?

Eric: Yes. Do you know how old he was when he died?

Ernie: I've no idea.

Eric: You won't believe this, but he was 147 years old.

Ernie: 147 years old?

Eric: And he never had a day's illness in his life.

Ernie: How about the day he died?

Eric: Well, I'll admit he wasn't feeling too good that day. However, about my Uncle Barney.

Ernie: I'd like to get some sleep.

Eric: My Uncle Barney discovered the secret of long life quite by accident in the Outer Hebrides.

Ernie: The Outer Hebrides?

Eric: He should have gone to Torquay, but the coach driver lost his glasses.

Ernie: Just get on with it.

Eric: My Uncle Barney was in the Outer Hebrides and this old crofter told him the secret of long life.

Ernie: He did! He told him the secret of long life! What is it?

Eric: I'll tell you some other time. You're too tired now. Goodnight.

Ernie: No Eric, I'm not too tired, I must know the secret. You're quite right, I don't want to grow old. I must know the secret . . . please Eric!

Eric: Very well. Do you know what the old crofter told my Uncle Barney?

Ernie: Go on, go on!

Eric: He told my Uncle Barney the secret of long life.

Ernie: Which is? Go on!

Eric: Are you sure you don't fancy a wine gum?

Ernie: No, what did he tell him? What did he say was the secret of long life?

Eric: Puffins.

Ernie: Puffins?

Eric: Puffins, you know, sea birds. The old crofter said to my Uncle Barney, 'A puffin a day keeps the doctor away' – and a lot of other people as well, I'm told. Anyway, my Uncle Barney gave it a try.

Ernie: And?

Eric: You won't believe this. Do you know how old he was when he died?

Ernie: How old was he?

Eric: 23.

Ernie: 23!

Eric: He fell 300 feet off a cliff trying to catch a puffin. So it must be the cliffs you have to watch, not the puffins.

Ernie: Pass me a wine gum!

Getting Married

(Eric and Ernie are sitting on the settee. Eric is reading a newspaper, Ernie is reading a book.)

Eric: There's a man here in Preston who drank a bottle of bleach. He's in hospital now.

Ernie: How is he?

Eric: Fair. There's a man here who got fined £50 by the RSPCA for knocking nails in with a tortoise.

Ernie: People are no longer kind.

Eric: I'm fed up. Do you fancy a game of blow football?

Ernie: No thank you.

Eric: Because of what happened last time we played?

Ernie: That's nothing to do with it.

Eric: I blew too hard, didn't I? I blew it right off your head. I'll never forget the look on your face as it shot under the table.

Ernie: Very funny.

Eric: And you sitting there, like an egg.

Ernie: You like to insult me, don't you?

Eric: Yes, thank you.

(*The doorbell rings.*)

Ernie: Go and answer it.

Eric: Certainly.

(*Crosses to the table and picks up the phone.*)

Ernie: It's somebody at the door.

Eric: I can't talk to you now. There's somebody at the door.

(*Opens the door. There's a Vicar standing there.*)

Vicar: Good morning. My name is Perkins.

Eric: Well you can't win 'em all.

(*Slams the door in the Vicar's face.*)

Ernie: Who was it?

Eric: Now that's what I call being friendly. A stranger knocks at our front door just to tell us his name is Perkins.

Ernie: Perkins? Oh no! (*Crosses to the door and opens it.*) I'm terribly sorry, Vicar, come in.

(*Vicar enters.*)

Vicar: Good morning, Mr Wise. (*Sees Eric.*) I don't think we've met.

Ernie: I'm sorry, Vicar. This is Mr Morecambe.

Vicar: (*Shaking Eric's hand.*) Mr Morecambe.

Eric: Your vicarship.

Ernie: Do come in and sit down, Vicar.

(*Moves to the couch.*)

Eric: If you've called for money for the church roof, we'll give you what we can – which isn't much, as you can see from this slum.

Ernie: The Vicar hasn't called for money for the church roof.

Eric: The Oxfam clothing? Thank you very much, Vicar. But could I have size 15½ shirts next time? I go a funny colour when I try to fasten those fifteens.

Ernie: Look Eric, the Vicar has called to see me about something else. Something personal.

Eric: Sorry. Before you start, do you fancy a drink Mr Vicar?

Vicar: That's very kind of you.

Eric: Scotch, gin, vodka, you name it.

Vicar: You don't happen to have any apple wine, do you?

Eric: It's funny you should say that. No, we don't.

Vicar: In that case I'll have a dry sherry.

Eric: Ern?

Ernie: A sweet Martini.

Eric: One sweet Martini, and a sherry for the Vicar. (*Brings drinks over.*) Do you save wicked women?

Vicar: Yes.

Eric: Save one for me. (*Laughs*)

Vicar: Now Mr Wise, just to make quite sure I have things right. It is the 25th, isn't it?

Ernie: That's right, Vicar, Saturday the 25th.

Vicar: At three o'clock in the afternoon?

Ernie: Three o'clock it is, Vicar.

Vicar: So Saturday the 25th at three o'clock is your big day. Now what about cars and the hire of the hall after?

Ernie: I've seen to all that, Vicar.

Vicar: I suppose you're feeling nervous, Mr Wise?

Ernie: Yes. Who wouldn't be?

Vicar: It isn't the sort of thing one does every day. No backing out now?

Ernie: I wouldn't dream of it, Vicar.

Vicar: I've been to see your bride-to-be – a charming girl. You're a very lucky man.

Ernie: I know.

Vicar: I'm sure you'll both be very happy.

Ernie: I know we will be.

Vicar: Have you found anywhere to live yet?

Ernie: After we're married we'll live here in the flat.

Vicar: Very nice. Just you and your lovely bride.

Ernie: Yes, it will be . . . just the two of us here together.

Vicar: (*Gets up*) Everything seems to be all right then. I have a lot to do.

Ernie: (*Shaking hands with the Vicar.*) Thank you very much for calling, Vicar.

Vicar: Not at all. See you on Saturday, Mr Wise. (*Shakes hands with Eric.*) Goodbye, Mr Morecambe.

Eric: Get out. (*Pushes Vicar through the door.*)

Ernie: Now I must make a list of all the guests. (*Writing*) Mr and Mrs Thomas . . . .

Eric: Ern? You're not, are you, Ern?

Ernie: I'm not what?

Eric: Getting married?

Ernie: I certainly am – Saturday the 25th at three o'clock.

Eric: What about *me*, Ern?

Ernie: What *about* you?

Eric: You just told the Vicar you'd be living here . . . just the two of you.

Ernie: That's right.

Eric: I won't have anywhere to live, Ern. Where will *I* live? You wouldn't let them put me in a home, would you, Ern?

Ernie: I couldn't care less.

Eric: You couldn't be that cruel.

Ernie: You can go and stay at your Auntie Winnie's.

Eric: How can I go to my Auntie Winnie's? She's always drunk.

Ernie: You'll have to get a council house.

Eric: I can't pay the rent.

Ernie: I'm sorry but I'm getting married and that's that.

Eric: You can't get married. You haven't got the wind. Anyway, your legs have gone.

Ernie: Saturday the 25th at three o'clock.

Eric: Will it be on *Match of the Day*?

Ernie: Make the most of your insults while you can.

Eric: It's a joke, isn't it Ern? That wasn't the Vicar. It was one of your mates dressed up just to try and fool me, wasn't it, Ern?

Ernie: He's no actor. I told you you'd be sorry for the way you've treated me.

Eric: It was only in fun, Ern.

Ernie: Now who shall I have for my best man? (*Thinking*)

(*The doorbell rings.*)

Ernie: I think this is for me.

(*Crosses, opens door and sees girl.*)

Hetty: Ernie, darling!

Ernie: Sweetheart! (*Puts arms around Hetty*) Come in, darling.

(*Hetty enters*)

Hetty: Hello, Eric.

Eric: That's not her, is it Ern?

Ernie: What do you mean?

Eric: It's Hetty, Hetty Benson! You're not serious about this are you, Ern? I remember her when we were all at school together.

Ernie: Be quiet!

Eric: She'd show you her garters for a lick of your lollipop.

Hetty: I've just been for a fitting for my wedding dress, darling. You'll love me in it.

Ernie: I love you anyway, Hetty, my sweet. I was just trying to think who I could have for my best man.

Hetty: What about my brother, Bob?

Ernie: What a good idea.

Eric: Is he out now?

Ernie: Don't take any notice of him, my little angel cake.

Eric: You're going to have your hands full with him, I can tell you.

Hetty: Well, we all have our funny little ways.

Eric: And his are the funniest little ways you ever saw!

Ernie: Go away.

Eric: Has she seen you with it off yet? (*Points to Ernie's hair*) Go on! Give her a quick flash, now. I dare you.

Hetty: Darling, what is he talking about?

Ernie: Just take no notice of him, my little flower.

Hetty: Of course, darling. Oh, how I'm looking forward to our honeymoon.

Eric: You're in for a shock there, I can tell you.

Ernie: Nobody's asking you.

Eric: Take a good book with you.

Ernie: That'll do.

Eric: Shall I tell her why they turned you down for the army?

Ernie: Take no notice. We'll be leaving soon, anyway.

Hetty: Darling, have you fixed a place to stay?

Ernie: (*Shy*) Yes, it's . . . it's one of those honeymoon hotels.

Eric: I can just see him on your wedding night sitting up in bed, shaved, hair combed, new silk pyjamas on . . . .

Hetty: He'll look so handsome.

Eric: It'll be a shame to wake him. It's going to be a bit crowded in that bed with the three of you.

Hetty: Three of us?

(*Eric gets the teddy bear*)

Eric: Hasn't he told you about Teddy yet? His auntie gave it to him when he was a little girl.

Ernie: Get out of this flat now!

Eric: (*To Hetty*) You heard him, get out of this flat now.

Ernie: Not her, you!

Eric: Let me stay.

Hetty: Certainly not.

Eric: I promise I won't look. I'll laugh but I won't look.

Ernie: When we moved into this flat we agreed that the one who gets married first gets the flat. The other one has to move out.

(*Eric moves back.*)

Eric: And you're sticking to that?

Ernie: I'm sticking to that.

Eric: Well, you'd better get packed.

Ernie: Why?

Eric: Because I married Maggie Fairfax this morning. Come in Maggie.

(*Opens the door and Maggie enters. Hetty bursts into tears and rushes over to Ernie.*)

Ernie: It makes you sick.

Eric: (*Worried*) It doesn't, does it?